Blessed Be

 TO

by Terri Wilson

ISBN: 978-0-9916711-4-4
www.yaada.pub

Tall and straight as the ash tree grows
All the things Athena knows
Smooth and sharp as an athame blade
All the color of an autumn glade

B

Fires at Beltane, jumping high
Watch the bees buzzing by
A silver bell ringing bright
A besom sweep makes it right

Stir a cauldron, round and round
Cast a circle on the ground
Catch a crystal in your hand
Light a candle if you can

A raven dips and dives in the dark
Demeter makes things grow in the park
Dragon dozing in his lair
Dance with delight, do as you dare

In the early east, an eagle flies
In an elder elm, her one egg lies
Energy comes from elements four
Embrace them all, open each door

Flight and a feather, often together
Fish and fin, go for a swim
Light a fire, flames grow higher
Find a fox, on nature walks

The God and Goddess are all around
From sky above to grass on the ground
Grab a goblet, give a toast
Visit a grave to honor the ghost

Horus hears as a hawk flies high
Hemlock hills are rolling by
Share some happiness with a hug
Sit on Hestia's warm hearth rug

Isis whispers in the night
Is there incense left to light?
Sprites and imps will skip around
Inner spirit can be found

Catch a firefly in a jelly jar
Jump for joy when you see that star
Enjoy a summer day in June
Join your hands under the moon

I like when Magick is in the air
When kids get kisses in their hair
Cats and kittens, on your knee
Together like a lock and key

Love at Litha lets flowers bloom
A little laughter lifts a room
Loki plays a silly joke
Light a lamp and blow the smoke

The Morrigan smiles under May's moon
Tomorrow sometimes comes too soon
Maiden, mother and then the crone
Making mischief all alone

Pine needles in the wood
Nearby nests sit snug and good
Notice knots, they hold in power
Midnight nears, that's the hour

Osiris has two but Odin only one
Color eggs at Ostara, that's always fun
Only in the Otherworld do goblins stroll
Don't get confused, a goblin's not a troll

Poseidon likes to play in the deep
A pile of puppies makes a cute heap
The pentacle protects sacred spaces
Pansies and petunias have pretty faces

Porcupine has quills, arrows in a quiver
Quite cold in winter, quick to shiver
Call the quarters, salute the Queen
Ask the question that is never seen

Relax when you are reading runes
A raven calls out raucous tunes
Write a ritual for Friday morn
That red rose may have a thorn

Basking in the Solstice sun
Warming like a sticky bun
Smudging sage smells so sweet
Slithering snakes have no feet

 Teas and tinctures, talismans galore
Thoth likes books more than Thor
Water trickles down the stream
Try some Tarot, what does it mean?

Ugly umbrellas raised up high
Thunder rumbles in the sky
Venus on a unicorn
Out of bubbles she was born

Nike votes for victory
Volcanoes and Pele across the sea
Valkyries to Valhalla fly
Vanilla for love, give it a try

Make a wish on a western wind
With a wand, wild women grinned
Witches, Wiccans, warlocks too
In the winter, owls ask who

A pixie relaxes in the wood
Jinxes and hexes are never good
With equinox, the days are split
With waxing moon, the night is lit

Both holly and yew are right for Yule
You'll find nymphs by yonder pool
Yarrow and tansy in a vase
Sitting on some yellow lace

Zeus in a fez, do what he says
Zebras in zoos, time for a snooze
Wander the maze, the ancient ways
Need for some zen? Just say when